DATE DUE

JUN 17 1986			
MAR 21 1998			

THE BEST ... FREE
AT YOUR

SOLDIER SONGS
AND HOME-FRONT BALLADS
OF THE CIVIL WAR

Compiled and Edited by Irwin Silber

OAK PUBLICATIONS NEW YORK, N.Y.

Music Editor: Jerry Silverman
Cover Design: Ronald Clyne

165 West 46th St., New York, N. Y.

LIBRARY OF CONGRESS CARD # 64-23697

Printed in the United States of America
for the Publisher by Faculty Press, Inc., Brooklyn, N. Y.

CONTENTS

Our troops marching down into the trenches before Richmond

For Moses Asch

who tended the flame
long before most of us
knew there was a fire

Making A Cremona

INTRODUCTION

The Civil War, that great fratricidal conflict which played such a decisive role in shaping our history and our national consciousness, exists no longer in the first-hand memories of living men. The aging, gray-haired veterans, whose grand reunions and garrulous recollections were, for so many decades, living reminders of the Civil War, have all crossed over into Jordan. The memories of the Civil War are now dependent on less fragile material—on histories and biographies, on the printed page and the time-worn photograph, on artists' sketches and such minute memorabilia as wartime maps, fading uniforms, medals (some tarnished, some still shining), bayonets, swords, battle flags, and other material objects, trifling and important, of an age gone by, which remain after human flesh has paid its inevitable price to mortality.

Among our less tangible but no less real keepsakes, however, are the songs of the Civil War—the stirring marching songs and patriotic hymns, the unabashedly sentimental ballads and the comic ditties, the boasting songs and drinking songs and fighting songs and loving songs of America's bloodiest and most significant struggle. And through these songs, an age which is past is brought to life, and we live with the men and women who walked this land of ours a century ago.

The music of the Civil War is more than a succession of lyrics and melodies bounded by Sumter and Appomattox. For nineteenth-century America was a youngster among nations, a brash adolescent emerging from the long shaow of European tradition and culture, the smoke from its newly sprung factories fashioning a soot-grimed image against the stars, the burgeoning music of steam whistles and pounding engines and slave cries giving birth to melodies and tunes and manners of speech which the world would soon call "American."

In 1861, in those fierce and turbulent months when the Union was falling apart, America's music was struggling to break through the thick crust of its European legacy. True, for the two decades preceding the Civil War, a few gifted tune smiths had begun to write a new kind of music. It was a zestful, lively, tuneful, rhythmic music composed of plaintive plantation chants and energetic pioneer shouts, seasoned liberally with a healthy dash of Irish and Scottish melody, with traces of French and German song idioms occasionally audible. Such men as Stephen Collins Foster and Daniel Decatur Emmett had discovered the rich melodic and rhythmic patterns of the Southern Negro and had begun to fashion them into a music which the world had never heard before. On the minstrel stages in the big cities and in small meetinghouses on the lonesome frontier, an indigenous American music was growing.

But this new music was still only a small voice in the American consciousness. A country whose national songs were created in another land and age, whose composers and poets were, by and large, inheritors of musical and literary styles and idioms not of their own making, was only tentatively reaching for its own form of expression.

A process which might have lasted for generations was underway, and none could foresee its outcome. But the Civil War, with its military and political urgencies, with its grand mixing of backgrounds and cultures, with its need for songs of inspiration and sorrow and laughter, and with its focus on the inner meaning of the American Union acted as a catalyst in the development of our music, and the hitherto slow process of Americanization was suddenly squeezed into a few short years. As the Civil War liberated the Negro slave, it also liberated American music from its hidebound, alien tradition.

It was with the Civil War that the music of the Negro began to penetrate fully the national consciousness and play the decisive role it eventually assumed in the emergence of a distinctively American musical idiom, combining with the Scotch-Irish-Anglo-Saxon tradition which had been, up until then, the main form of musical expression of white America. It was, by no means, an overnight development. Many songs of Civil War America continued to reflect the European heritage. But where America of 1812-1814 produced, as its most lasting musical memory, the patriotic verses written to the melody of an old English drinking song, which eventually became our national anthem, from the Civil War emerged such undeniably American works (in both tune and lyric) as "John Brown's Body," "Dixie," "The Battle Cry of Freedom," and "Marching Through Georgia."

The four years of the Civil War produced a startling upheaval in the American idiom, decisively affecting literature, music, and all other forms of creative expression. No other war in American history has produced such a great variety of songs, nor such a quantity. In searching through library and personal manuscript collections, through aged and yellowing songsters and old newspapers, through folksong collections and regimental histories, I have seen some 10,000 songs which could legitimately be considered part of our Civil War literature.

These songs are among the raw materials of history. They are narrators of past events and a part of those very same events themselves. As repositories of historical information they are, more often than not, inaccurate and unreliable. But as barometers of the popular sentiments of their time, these Civil War songs and ballads are valuable indices to the past.

This particular collection is designed to make a representative selection of Civil War songs readily available to the public in a manner as close to the original as is historically possible. All of these songs are from the period of the Civil War itself. The versions are, wherever available, from contemporary sources. I have also drawn upon other first-hand sources for anecdotes and quotations which may help give an added dimension to each song.

For more extensive historical notes on the songs, I refer the reader to my book, "Songs of the Civil War," published by Columbia University Press (1960), $7.50. This volume contains considerable historical data on the material, as well as piano settings for each song. More than half of the songs in this collection have been recorded on Folkways' "Songs of the Civil War" (FH5717).

In two cases ("Dixie" and "Kingdom Coming") I have "translated" the lyrics from the dated minstrel dialect of the period to manageable English, since the perpetuation of the dishonest "Negro" stereotype implied in the original is eminently offensive and distasteful in a work of this kind. The "dialect versions" may be found in the Columbia University Press study.

Many singers and collectors have made their efforts in this area available to me. Among these, I wish to thank particularly Ben Botkin, Walter Lowenfels, Frank Warner, Ellen Stekert, Hermes Nye, Alan Lomax, and Waldemar Hille. Much of this material came from resources at The Library of Congress in Washington, D. C., The New York Public Library, and The Philadelphia Library, and I wish to acknowledge my appreciation of the various librarians at these institutions for their assistance and cooperation in my researches. Jerry Silverman was an invaluable co-worker on the original study and his work is indelibly inscribed in the pages of this collection as well.

A song on a printed page is only a series of hen-scratches The song becomes a song only when it is sung. Sing these songs, then, remembering that each note, each word was a moment of historical experience multiplied many times over during one of the crucial and decisive eras of our history as a people.

New York, N. Y.
January, 1964 Irwin Silber

Recruiting for the war. Scene at the recruiting tents in the park, New York

Johnny Is My Darling

Words by Father Reed
Music: "Charlie Is My Darling"

It was toward the end of the terrible struggle between the States. A weary and dusty Confederate sat cooling his tired feet in a stream, while, with a rusty needle and coarse thread he was endeavoring to mend his ragged coat. Suddenly a mounted Federal dashed into view, and riding rapidly toward the Confederate, he shouted: "Hi, there, Johnny Reb, I've got you this time."

Without looking up from his mending the half-starved, ragged and dirty fellow replied: "Yes, and a hell of a git you got."

—*Confederate Women of Arkansas in the Civil War, 1861-'65, Memorial Reminiscences.*

2. As he came marching up the street,
   The bands played loud and clear;
   And everyone came out to greet
   The Union Volunteer. (Chorus)

3. With proudly waving starry flags
   And hearts that knew no fear;
   He came to fight for Freedom's rights,
   A Union Volunteer. (Chorus)

4. But though he s gone to glory win,
   And I left lonely here,
   He'll soon return to me again
   As *Cupid's Volunteer.* (Chorus)

Just Before the Battle, Mother

Words and music by George F. Root

The *Flying* Artillery of the C. S. A.

Cost what it may, every slave on the American soil must be liberated from his chains. Nothing is to be put in competition, on the score of value, with the price of his liberty; for whatever conflicts with the right of man must be evil, and therefore intrinsically worthless. . . . There must be no compromise with slavery—none whatever. Nothing is gained, everything is lost, by subordinating principle to expediency.

—*William Lloyd Garrison, in The Liberator.*

2. Oh, I long to see you, Mother,
   And the loving ones at home,
   But I'll never leave our banner,
   Till in honor I can come.
   Tell the traitors all around you
   That their cruel words we know,
   In every battle kill our soldiers
   By the help they give the foe. (Chorus)

3. Hark! I hear the bugles sounding,
   'Tis the signal for the fight,
   Now, may God protect us, Mother,
   As He ever does the right.
   Hear the "Battle Cry of Freedom,"
   How it swells upon the air,
   Oh, yes, we'll rally 'round the standard,
   Or we'll perish nobly there. (Chorus)

Farewell, Mother

Words: anonymous
Music: "Just Before the Battle, Mother"

> Article First: This company shall be known as the Bungtown Riflemen.
> Article Second: In case of war, this company shall immediately disband.
> —*By-Laws of the Bungtown (Ohio) Riflemen.*

1. Just before the battle, mother,
   I was drinking mountain dew,
   When I saw the "Rebels" marching,
   To the rear I quickly flew;
   Where the stragglers were flying,
   Thinking of their homes and wives;
   'Twas not the "Reb" we feared, dear mother,
   But our own dear precious lives.

2. I hear the bugle sounding, mother,
   My soul is eager for the fray.
   I guess I'll hide behind some cover,
   And then I shall be O.K.
   Discretion's the better part of valor,
   At least I've often heard you say;
   And he who loves his life, dear mother,
   Won't fight if he can run away. (Chorus)

Chorus: Farewell, mother! for you'll never
See my name among the slain.
For if I only can skedaddle,
Dear mother, I'll come home again.

Brother Green

Words: anonymous
Music: "Barbara Allen"
From the singing of Mrs. Emma Dusenberry

Swift blazing flag of the regiment,
Eagle with crest of red and gold,
These men were born to drill and die.
Point for them the virtue of slaughter,
Make plain to them the excellence of killing
And a field where a thousand corpses lie.
—*Stephen Crane, from "War Is Kind."*

2. The Southern foe has laid me low,
On this cold ground to suffer,
Dear brother stay, and put me away,
And write my wife a letter.

3. Tell her I know she's prayed for me,
And now her prayers are answered,
That I might be prepared to die
If I should fall in battle.

4. Go tell my wife she must not grieve,
Go kiss my little children,
For I am going to Heaven to live
To see my dear old mother.

Dear sister may have gone there, too,
She lives and reigns with angels,
And Jeffer's son who died when young,
I know I'll see their faces.

6. I have one brother in this wide world,
He's fighting for the Union,
But oh, dear wife, I've lost my life,
To put down this Rebellion.

7. Tell my wife she must not grieve,
And kiss the little children,
For they will call their pa in vain,
When he is up in Heaven.

8. My little babes, I love them well,
Oh could I once more see them,
That I might give a long farewell
And meet them all in Heaven.

Old Abe Lincoln Came Out of the Wilderness

Words: anonymous
Music: "Down in Alabam" (by J. Warner)

Gentlemen, Fellow-Citizens. I presume you all know who I am. I am humble Abraham Lincoln. I have been solicited by many friends to become a candidate for the legislature. My politics are short and sweet, like an old woman's dance. I am in favor of a National Bank. I am in favor of the internal improvement system, and a high protective tariff. These are my sentiments and political principles. If elected, I shall be thankful; if not, it will be all the same.

—*Abraham Lincoln, Sangamon County, 1832.*

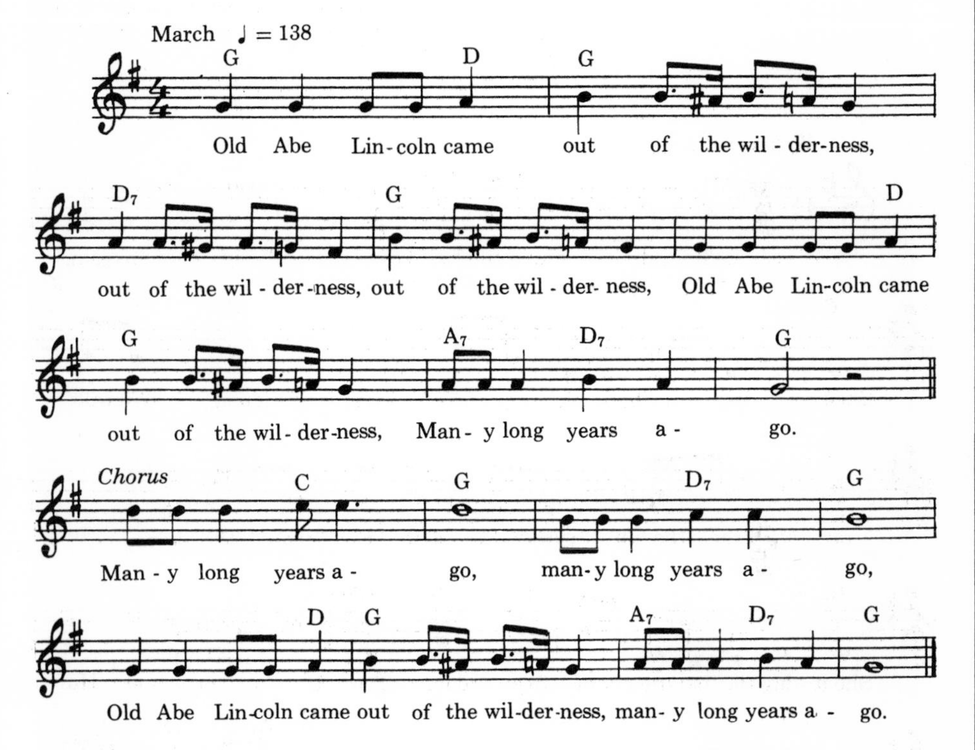

2. Old Jeff Davis tore down the government,
tore down the government,
tore down the government,
Old Jeff Davis tore down the government,
Many long years ago. (Chorus)

3. But old Abe Lincoln built up a better one,
built up a better one,
built up a better one,
Old Abe Lincoln built up a better one,
Many long years ago. (Chorus)

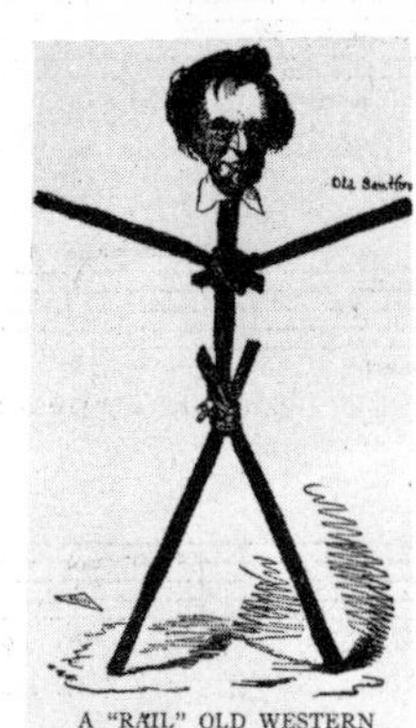

A "RAIL" OLD WESTERN GENTLEMAN

The Battle Cry of Freedom

Words and music by George F. Root

New-York Daily Tribune

SUNDAY, JUNE 30, 1861.

THE NATION'S WAR-CRY.

Forward to Richmond! Forward to Richmond! The Rebel Congress must not be allowed to meet there on the 20th of July! BY THAT DATE THE PLACE MUST BE HELD BY THE NATIONAL ARMY!

I shall never forget the first time that I heard 'Rally Round the Flag.' It was a nasty night during the "Seven Days Fight," and, if I remember rightly, it was raining. I was on picket when, just before taps, some fellow on the other side struck up that song and others joined in the chorus until it seemed to me the whole Yankee Army was singing. Tom B——, who was with me, sung out: "Good Heavens, cap, what are those fellows made of anyway? Here we've licked 'em six days running, and now on the eve of the seventh, they're singing 'Rally Round the Flag.' I am not naturally superstitious, but I tell you that song sounded to me like the knell of doom, and my heart went down into my boots; and though I've tried to do my duty, it has been an uphill fight with me ever since that."—*A Confederate Major, writing shortly after the Civil War.*

2. We are springing to the call of our brothers gone before,
   Shouting the battle cry of freedom,
   And we'll fill the vacant ranks with a million freemen more,
   Shouting the battle cry of freedom. (Chorus)

3. We will welcome to our numbers the loyal, true, and brave,
   Shouting the battle cry of freedom,
   And although they may be poor not a man shall be a slave,
   Shouting the battle cry of freedom. (Chorus)

4. So we're springing to the call from the East and from the West,
   Shouting the battle cry of freedom,
   And we'll hurl the Rebel crew from the land we love the best,
   Shouting the battle cry of freedom. (Chorus)

The Brass-Mounted Army

Words: an anonymous soldier of
Col. A. Buchel's Regiment
Music: adapted from "Wait for the Wagon"

A Union gunboat was just about to go into action when the deck officer came upon one soldier on his knees. The officer asked him if he was afraid.

"No, I was praying," was the soldier's response.

"Well, what were you praying for?" asked the officer.

"Praying," said the soldier, "that the enemy's bullets may be distributed in the same way as the prize money is, *principally among the officers.*"

2. Whisky is a monster, and ruins great and small,
   But in our noble army, Headquarters gets it all;
   They drink it when there's danger, although it seems too hard,
   But if a private touches it they put him "under guard." (Chorus)

3. And when we meet the ladies we're bound to go it sly,
   Headquarters are the pudding, and the privates are the pie!
   They issue Standing Orders to keep us all in line,
   For if *we* had a showing, the *brass* would fail to shine. (Chorus)

4. At every big plantation or Negro-holder's yard,
Just to save the property, the general puts a guard;
The sentry's then instructed to let no private pass—
The rich man's house and table are fixed to suit the "brass." (Chorus)

5. I have to change this story, so beautiful and true,
But the poor man and widow must have a line or two;
For them no guard is stationed, their fences oft are burned,
And property molested, as long ago you've learned. (Chorus)

6. The army's now much richer than when the war begun,
It furnishes three tables where once it had but one;
The first is richly loaded with chickens, goose, and duck,
The rest with pork and mutton, the third with good old buck. (Chorus)

7. Our generals eat the poultry, and buy it very cheap,
Our colonels and our majors devour the hog and sheep;
The privates are contented (except when they can steal),
With beef and corn bread plenty to make a hearty meal. (Chorus)

8. Sometimes we get so hungry that we're bound to press a pig,
Then the largest stump in Dixie we're sure to have to dig;
And when we fret, an officer who wears long-legged boots,
With neither judge nor jury, puts us on "double roots." (Chorus)

9. These things, and many others, are truly hard to me,
But still I'll be contented, and fight for Liberty!
And when the war is over, oh what a jolly time!
We'll be our own commanders and sing much sweeter rhymes. (Chorus)

10. We'll see our loving sweethearts, and sometimes kiss them too,
We'll eat the finest rations, and bid old buck adieu;
There'll be no generals with orders to compel,
Long boots and eagle buttons, forever fare ye well!

Final Chorus:

And thus we'll leave the army, the brass-mounted army,
The high-faluting army, where eagle buttons rule.

Pat Murphy of the Irish Brigade

Anonymous

This day will be remembered by America's noble sons,
If it hadn't a-been for Irishmen, what would our Union done?
'Twas hand to hand we fought 'em all in the broiling sun,
Stripped to the pants we did advance at the Battle of Bull Run!

—from the singing of Frank Warner as learned from Yankee John Galusha.

2. The morning soon broke and poor Paddy awoke,
He found Rebels to give satisfaction,
And the drummers were beating the Devil's sad tune,
They were calling the boys into action. (Chorus)

3. Sure, the day after battle, the dead lay in heaps,
And Pat Murphy lay bleeding and gory,
With a hole through his head by some enemy's ball
That ended his passion for glory. (Chorus)

4. No more in the camp will his letters be read,
Or his song be heard singing so gaily,
But he died far away from the friends that he loved,
And far from the land of shillelagh. (Chorus)

Father Mooney saying mass for the 69th New York State Militia in Virginia, 1861. *By Brady or assistant*

The Cumberland Crew

Anonymous

THE UNITED STATES SLOOP "CUMBERLAND"

Ho! brave hearts that went down in the seas,
Ye are at peace in the troubled stream,
Ho! brave land! with hearts like these,
Thy flag that is rent in twain,
Shall be one again,
And without a seam.

—*Henry Wadsworth Longfellow,*
from "The Cumberland"

2. That ill-fated day, about ten in the morning,
The sky it was cloudless and bright shone the sun;
The drums of the Cumberland sounded a warning
That told every man to stand by his gun.
When an iron-clad frigate down on us came bearing,
High up in the air her base Rebel flag flew;
An emblem of treason she proudly was wearing,
Determined to conquer the Cumberland Crew.

3. They fought us three hours with stern resolution,
Till those Rebels found cannon could never decide;
For the flag of Secession had no power to quell them,
Though the blood from our scuppers did crimson the tide.
She struck us amidships, our planks she did sever,
Her sharp iron prow pierced our noble ship through;
And slowly we sank in Virginia's dark waters,
"We'll die by our guns," cried the Cumberland Crew.

4. Oh, slowly she sank in the dark rolling waters,
Their voices on earth will be heard never more.
They'll be wept by Columbia's brave sons and fair daughters,
May their blood be avenged on Virginia's old shore.
And if ever sailors in battle assemble,
God bless our dear banner—the red, white, and blue;
Beneath its proud folds we'll cause tyrants to tremble,
Or sink at our guns like the Cumberland Crew.

THE "MERRIMAC" RAMMING THE "CUMBERLAND."

Go Down, Moses

Traditional Negro spiritual

JEFF. AND HIS PET

I did not, when a slave, understand the deep meanings of those rude, and apparently incoherent songs. I was myself within the circle, so that I neither saw nor heard as those without might see and hear. They told a tale which was then altogether beyond my feeble comprehension: they were tones, loud, long and deep, breathing the prayer and complaint of souls boiling over with the bitterest anguish. Every tone was a testimony against slavery, and a prayer to God for deliverance from chains.

—*Frederick Douglass, Autobiography.*

2. Thus saith the Lord, bold Moses said,
   Let my people go,
   If not, I'll smite your first-born dead,
   Let my people go. (Chorus)

3. No more shall they in bondage toil,
   Let them come out with Egypt's spoil.
   (Chorus)

4. The Lord told Moses what to do,
   To lead the Hebrew children through.
   (Chorus)

5. O come along Moses, you'll not get lost,
   Stretch out your rod and come across.
   (Chorus)

6. As Israel stood by the waterside,
   At God's command it did divide.
   (Chorus)

7. When they reached the other shore,
   They sang a song of triumph o'er.
   (Chorus)

8. Pharaoh said he'd go across,
   But Pharaoh and his host were lost.
   (Chorus)

9. Jordan shall stand up like a wall,
   And the walls of Jericho shall fall.
   (Chorus)

10. Your foes shall not before you stand,
And you'll possess fair Canaan's Land.
(Chorus)

11. O let us all from bondage flee,
And let us all in Christ be free.
(Chorus)

12. We need not always weep and mourn,
And wear these slavery chains forlorn.
(Chorus)

The Yellow Rose of Texas

Anonymous

"If I owned Texas and hell, I would rent Texas and move to hell," said a famous general.
"That's right," wrote a Texas editor. "Every man for his own country."
—*Carl Sandburg, The People Yes.*

Spirited march ♩ = 120

A
There's a yel - low rose in Tex - as that I am going to see, No
E7
oth - er sol - dier knows her, no sol - dier, on - ly me; She
A
cried so when I left her, it like to broke my heart, And
E7 A E7 A
if I ev - er find her, we nev - er more will part.

Chorus
She's the sweet - est rose of col - or this sol - dier ev - er knew, Her
E7
eyes are bright as dia - monds, they spar - kle like the dew; You may
A
talk a - bout your dear - est May and sing of Ro - sa Lee, But the
E7 B7 A E7 A
Yel - low Rose of Tex - as beats the belles of Ten - nes - see.

2. Where the Rio Grande is flowing and the starry skies are bright,
   She walks along the river in the quiet summer night;
   She thinks if I remember, when we parted long ago,
   I promised to come back again and not to leave her so. (Chorus)

3. Oh, now I'm going to find her, for my heart is full of woe,
   And we'll sing the song together, that we sung so long ago;
   We'll play the banjo gaily, and we'll sing the songs of yore,
   And the Yellow Rose of Texas shall be mine forevermore. (Chorus)

The Vacant Chair

Words by Henry S. Washburn
Music by George F. Root

STRIKE WITH AN IRON ARM FOR OUR WHOLE UNION!

The dead, the dead, the dead, our dead—or South or North—ours all (all, all, all finally dear to me), or East or West, Atlantic Coast or Mississippi Valley—somewhere they crawled to die alone—in bushes, low gullies, or on the sides of hills. . . . Our young men, once so handsome and so joyous, taken from us—the son from the mother, the husband from the wife, the dear friend from the dear friend—the clusters of many graves in Georgia, the Carolinas and in Tennessee. Everywhere among these countless graves—everywhere in the many soldiers' cemeteries of the nation—we see, and ages yet may see, on monuments and gravestones, singly or in masses to thousands or tens of thousands, the significant word UNKNOWN.

—*Walt Whitman.*

2. At our fireside, sad and lonely,
Often will the bosom swell
At remembrance of the story,
How our noble Willie fell;
How he strove to bear our banner
Through the thickest of the fight,
And uphold our country's honor,
In the strength of manhood's night. (Chorus)

3. True, they tell us wreaths of glory
Ever more will deck his brow,
But this soothes the anguish only,
Sweeping o'er our heartstrings now.
Sleep today, Oh early fallen,
In thy green and narrow bed,
Dirges from the pine and cypress
Mingle with the tears we shed. (Chorus)

There Was an Old Soldier

Traditional American folk song

In one of the regiments . . . I caught the bright face of a soldier leaning out from the lines as far as possible into the road, to catch the message that fell from my lips. "What is it? What is it?" he anxiously shouted. "Lee has surrendered with his whole army to Grant," was the reply. Clear and loud, above all the voices, and quick as the message fell upon his ears, was his answer: "Great God! You're the man I've been looking for for the last four years."

—*Captain A. J. Ricks*

2. Said the one old soldier, "Won't you give me a chew?"
Said the other old soldier, "I'll be hanged if I do,
Just save up your money and put away your rocks,
And you'll always have tobacco in your old tobacco box,
And you'll always have tobacco in your old tobacco box."

3. Well, the one old soldier, he was feeling mighty bad,
He said, "I'll get even, I will begad!"
He goes to a corner, takes a rifle from the peg,
And stabs the other soldier with a splinter from his leg,
And stabs the other soldier with a splinter from his leg.

4. Now there was an old hen and she had a wooden foot,
And she made her nest by the mulberry root,
She laid more eggs than any hen on the farm,
And another wooden leg wouldn't do her any harm.
And another wooden leg wouldn't do her any harm.

Oh Freedom

Traditional Negro spiritual

When the war ended, white man come to the field and tell my mother-in-law she free as he is. She dropped her hoe and danced up to the turn road and danced right up into Old Master's parlor. She went so fast a bird could a sat on her dress tail. That was in June. That night she sent and got all the neighbors, and they danced all night long.

—Eda Harper, former slave in Mississippi, interviewed in 1937 at the age of 93.

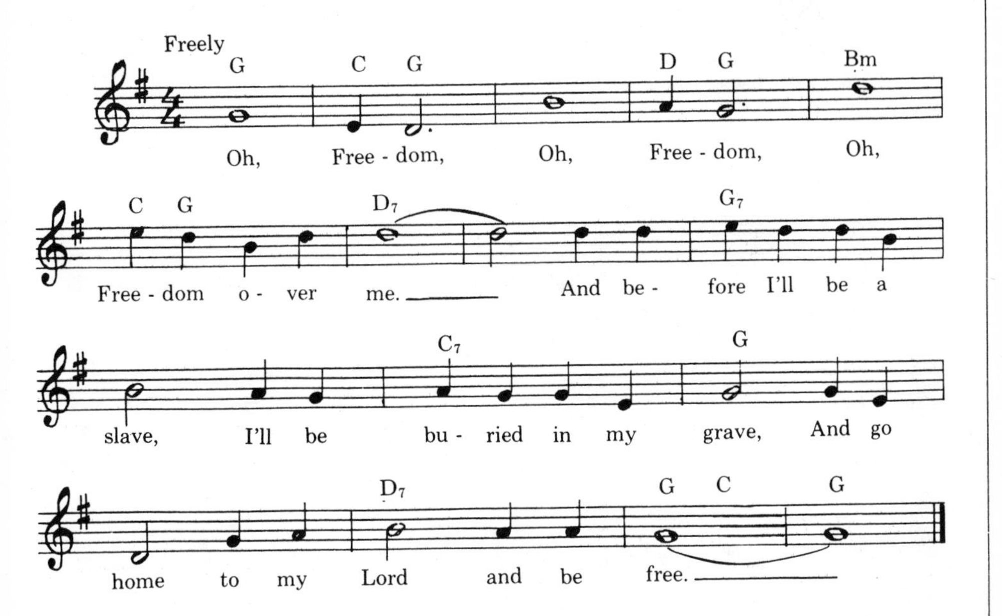

2. No more moaning, no more moaning,
   No more moaning over me.
   And before I'll be a slave,
   I'll be buried in my grave,
   And go home to my Lord and be free.

3. No more weeping, etc.

4. There'll be singing, etc.

TO BE SOLD on board the Ship *Bance-Yland*, on tuefday the 6th of *May* next, at *Afhley-Ferry*; a choice cargo of about 250 fine healthy

NEGROES,

juft arrived from the Windward & Rice Coaft. —The utmoft care has already been taken, and fhall be continued, to keep them free from the leaft danger of being infected with the SMALL-POX, no boat having been on board, and all other communication with people from *Charles-Town* prevented.

Auftin, Laurens, & Appleby.

N. B. Full one Half of the above Negroes have had the SMALL-POX in their own Country.

We'll Fight for Uncle Abe

Words by C. E. Pratt
Music by Frederick Buckley

Zouave.—"Uncle Abe will be glad to see you."

Jeff's March on Washington.
His courage kept up to the "sticking point."

Hush'd be the camps today,
And soldiers let us drape our war-worn weapons,
And each with musing soul retire to celebrate,
Our dear commander's death.
No more for him life's stormy conflicts,
Nor victory, nor defeat—no more time's dark events,
Charging like ceaseless clouds across the sky.
But sing poet in our name,
Sing of the love we bore him—because you—dweller in camps, know it truly.
As they invalut the coffin there,
Sing—as they close the doors of earth upon him—one verse,
For the heavy hearts of soldiers.

—Walt Whitman (May 4, 1865)

2. There is General Grant at Vicksburg,
Just see what he has done,
He has taken sixty cannon
And made the Rebels run,
And next he will take Richmond,
I'll bet you half a dollar,
And if he catches General Johnson,
Oh won't he make him holler. (Chorus)

3. The season now is coming
When the roads begin to dry;
Soon the Army of the Potomac
Will make the Rebels fly,
For General McClellan, he's the man,
The Union for to save;
Oh! Hail Columbia's right side up,
And so's your Uncle Abe. (Chorus)

4. You may talk of Southern chivalry
And cotton being king,
But I guess before the war is done
You'll think another thing;
They say that recognition
Will the Rebel country save,
But Johnny Bull and Mister France
Are 'fraid of Uncle Abe. (Chorus)

The Battle Hymn of the Republic

Words by Julia Ward Howe
Music: "John Brown's Body"

In spite of the excitement of the day I went to bed and slept as usual, but awoke next morning in the gray of the early dawn, and to my astonishment found that the wished-for lines were arranging themselves in my brain. I lay quite still until the last verse had completed itself in my thoughts, then hastily arose, saying to myself, "I shall lose this if I don't write it down immediately." I searched for an old sheet of paper and an old stump of a pen which I had had the night before, and began to scrawl the lines almost without looking, as I had learned to do by often scratching down verses in the darkened room where my little children were sleeping. Having completed this, I lay down again and fell asleep, but not without feeling that something of importance had happened to me.

—*Julia Ward Howe*

2. I have seen Him in the watch fires of a hundred circling camps;
   They have builded Him an altar in the evening dews and damps;
   I can read His righteous sentence by the dim and flaring lamps,
   His day is marching on. (Chorus)

3. I have read a fiery gospel writ in burnished rows of steel:
   "As ye deal with My contemners, so with you My Grace shall deal;
   Let the Hero, born of woman, crush the serpent with his heel,
   Since God is marching on." (Chorus)

4. He has sounded forth the trumpet that shall never call retreat;
   He is sifting out the hearts of men before His Judgment Seat;
   Oh! be swift, my soul, to answer Him, be jubilant, my feet!
   Our God is marching on. (Chorus)

5. In the beauty of the lilies Christ was born across the sea,
   With a glory in his bosom that transfigures you and me;
   As He died to make men holy, let us die to make men free,
   While God is marching on. (Chorus)

The march of the 7th New York

Marching Song of the First Arkansas (Negro) Regiment

Words ascribed to Capt. Lindley Miller
Music: "John Brown's Body"

Dark as the clouds of even,
Ranked in the western heaven,
Waiting the breath that lifts
All the dead mass, and drifts
Tempest and falling brand
Over a ruined land,—
So still and orderly,
Arm to arm, knee to knee,
Waiting the great event,
Stands the black regiment.
—*George H. Boker (May 27,1863).*

1. Oh, we're the bully soldiers of the "First of Arkansas,"
   We are fighting for the Union, we are fighting for the law,
   We can hit a Rebel further than a white man ever saw,
   As we go marching on.

Chorus:
Glory, glory hallelujah,
Glory, glory hallelujah,
Glory, glory hallelujah,
As we go marching on.

2. See, there above the center, where the flag is waving bright,
   We are going out of slavery; we're bound for freedom's light;
   We mean to show Jeff Davis how the Africans can fight,
   As we go marching on! (Chorus)

3. We have done with hoeing cotton, we have done with hoeing corn,
   We are colored Yankee soldiers, now, as sure as you are born;
   When the masters hear us yelling, they'll think it's Gabriel's horn,
   As we go marching on. (Chorus)

4. They will have to pay us wages, the wages of their sin,
   They will have to bow their foreheads to their colored kith and kin,
   They will have to give us house-room, or the roof shall tumble in!
   As we go marching on. (Chorus)

5. We heard the Proclamation, master hush it as he will,
   The bird he sing it to us, hoppin' on the cotton hill,
   And the possum up the gum tree, he couldn't keep it still,
   As he went climbing on. (Chorus)

6. They said, "Now colored brethren, you shall be forever free,
   From the first of January, Eighteen hundred sixty-three."
   We heard it in the river going rushing to the sea,
   As it went sounding on. (Chorus)

7. Father Abraham has spoken and the message has been sent,
   The prison doors he opened, and out the pris'ners went,
   To join the sable army of the "African descent,"
   As we go marching on. (Chorus)

8. Then fall in, colored brethren, you'd better do it soon,
   Don't you hear the drum a-beating the Yankee Doodle tune?
   We are with you now this morning, we'll be far away at noon,
   As we go marching on. (Chorus)

John Brown's Body

Words: anonymous
Music: "Say, Brothers, Will You Meet Us?"
(ascribed to William Steffe)

I am yet too young to understand that God is any respecter of persons. I believe that to have interfered as I have done . . . in behalf of His despised poor, was not wrong, but right. Now, if it is deemed necessary that I should forfeit my life for the furtherance of the ends of justice, and mingle my blood further with the blood of my children, and with the blood of millions in this slave country whose rights are disregarded by wicked, cruel, and unjust enactments, I submit: so let it be done!

—*John Brown, Last speech to the Court, Nov. 2, 1859.*

1. John Brown's body lies a-mouldering in the grave,
   John Brown's body lies a-mouldering in the grave,
   John Brown's body lies a-mouldering in the grave,
   But his soul goes marching on.

Chorus:

Glory; glory, hallelujah,
Glory, glory, hallelujah,
Glory, glory, hallelujah,
His soul goes marching on.

2. He's gone to be a soldier in the Army of the Lord,
   His soul goes marching on. (Chorus)

3. John Brown's knapsack is strapped upon his back,
   His soul goes marching on. (Chorus)

4. John Brown died that the slaves might be free,
   But his soul goes marching on. (Chorus)

5. The stars above in Heaven now are looking kindly down,
   On the grave of old John Brown. (Chorus)

Slavery Chain Done Broke at Last

Words: anonymous
Music: "Joshua Fit the Battle of Jericho"

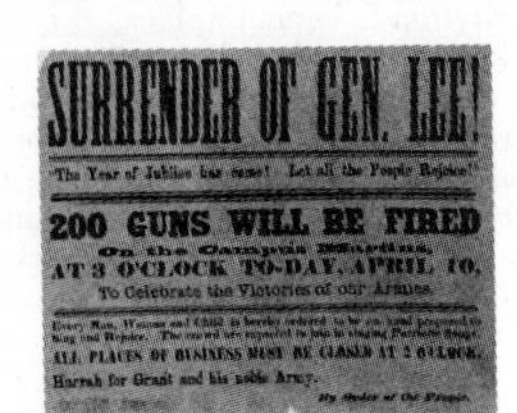

Once, to every man and nation,
Comes the moment to decide,
In the strife of truth with falsehood,
For the good or evil side;
Some great cause, God's *new* Messiah,
Offering each the bloom or blight,
Parts the goats upon the left hand,
And the sheep upon the right,
And the choice goes by forever
'Twixt that darkness and that light.
—James Russell Lowell, "The Present Crisis."

Jubilantly ♩ = 184

Em
Slav - e - ry chain — done — broke at last, —
Am B7
Broke at last, — Broke at last, ————
Em
Slav - e - ry chain done — broke at last, —
B7 Em *Fine*
Gon - na praise God till I die.

Chorus
Em B7 Em B7
Way up in that val - ley, Pray - in' on my knees,
Em B7 Em
Tell - in' God a - bout my trou - bles, And to help me if He please.
D.C. al Fine

2. I did tell him how I suffer,
   In the dungeon and the chain;
   And the days I went with head
   bowed down,
   An' my broken flesh and pain. (Chorus)

3. I did know my Jesus heard me,
   'Cause the spirit spoke to me,
   An' said, "Rise my chile, your children
   An' you too shall be free." (Chorus)

4. I done p'int one mighty captain
   For to marshall all my hosts;
   An' to bring my bleeding ones to me,
   An' not one shall be lost. (Chorus)

5. Now no more weary trav'lin',
   'Cause my Jesus set me free,
   An' there's no more auction block for me
   Since He give me liberty. (Chorus)

Weeping Sad and Lonely

Words by Charles C. Sawyer
Music by Henry Tucker

COUNTING THE SCARS IN THE COLORS.

There is nothing in this sentimental song that enables one to read the riddle of its remarkable popularity during the Civil War. It has no poetic merit; its rhythm is commonplace, and the tune to which it was sung was of the flimsiest musical structure, without even a trick of melody to commend it. Yet the song was more frequently sung, on both sides, than any other. . . . The thing was heard in every camp every day and many times every day. Men chanted it on the march, and women sang it to piano accompaniment in all houses. A song which so strongly appealed to two great armies and to an entire people is worthy of a place in all collections of war poetry, even though criticism is baffled in the attempt to discover the reason of its popularity.

—*George Cary Eggleston, "American War Ballads and Lyrics" (1889).*

2. When the summer breeze is sighing
Mournfully along;
Or when autumn leaves are falling,
Sadly breathes the song.
Oft in dreams I see thee lying
On the battle plain,
Lonely, wounded, even dying,
Calling but in vain. (Chorus)

3. If amid the din of battle,
Nobly you should fall,
Far away from those who love you,
None to hear you call,
Who would whisper words of comfort,
Who would soothe your pain?
Ah! the many cruel fancies
Ever in my brain. (Chorus)

4. But our country called you, darling,
Angels cheer your way;
While our nation's sons are fighting,
We can only pray.
Nobly strike for God and liberty,
Let all nations see,
How we love the starry banner,
Emblem of the free. (Chorus)

We Are Coming, Father Abr'am

Words by James Sloan Gibbons
Music by L. O. Emerson

No man is good enough to govern another man without that other's consent.
—*Abraham Lincoln.*

2. If you look across the hilltops
   That meet the northern sky,
   Long moving lines of rising dust
   Your vision may descry;
   And now the wind, an instant,
   Tears the cloudy veil aside,
   And floats aloft our spangled flag
   In glory and in pride;
   And bayonets in the sunlight gleam,
   And bands brave music pour.
   We are coming, Father Abr'am,
   Three hundred thousand more! (Chorus)

3. If you look all up our valleys
   Where the growing harvests shine,
   You may see our sturdy farmer boys
   Fast forming into line;
   And children from their mother's knees
   Are pulling at the weeds,
   And learning how to reap and sow
   Against their country's needs;
   And a farewell group stands weeping
   At every cottage door.
   We are coming, Father Abr'am,
   Three hundred thousand more! (Chorus)

4. You have called us and we're coming
   By Richmond's bloody tide,
   To lay us down for Freedom's sake,
   Our brothers' bones beside;
   Or from foul treason's savage group,
   To wrench the murderous blade;
   And in the face of foreign foes
   Its fragments to parade;
   Six hundred thousand loyal men
   And true have gone before.
   We are coming, Father Abr'am,
   Three hundred thousand more! (Chorus)

Overtures from Richmond

Words by Francis J. Child
Music: "Lilliburlero"

JEFF. DAVIS on the March.

Ther's critters yit thet talk an' act
Fer wut they call Conciliation;
They'd hand a buff'lo-drove a tract
When they wuz madder than all Bashan.
Conciliate? It jest means *be kicked*,
No metter how they phrase an' tone it;
It means that we're to sit down licked,
That we're poor shotes—an' glad to own it.
Hosea Biglow.
—James Russell Lowell

2. "So, Uncle Sam, just lay down your arms,"
   Lilliburlero, old Uncle Sam,
   "Then you shall hear my reas'nable terms,"
   Lilliburlero, old Uncle Sam.
   "Lero, lero, I'd like to hear-o
   I'd like to hear," says old Uncle Sam,
   "Lero, lero, filibuster-o,
   I'd like to hear," says old Uncle Sam.

3. "First you must own I've beat you in fight,"
Lilliburlero, old Uncle Sam,
"Then that I always have been in the right,"
Lilliburlero, old Uncle Sam.
"Lero, lero, rather severe-o
Rather severe," says old Uncle Sam,
"Lero, lero, filibuster-o,
Rather severe," says old Uncle Sam.

4. "Then you must pay my national debts,"
Lilliburlero, old Uncle Sam,
"No questions asked about my assets,"
Lilliburlero, old Uncle Sam.
"Lero, lero, that's very dear-o
That's very dear," says old Uncle Sam,
"Lero, lero, filibuster-o,
That's very dear," says old Uncle Sam.

5. "Also some few IOU's and bets,"
Lilliburlero, old Uncle Sam,
"Mine, and Bob Toombs', and Sidell's and Rhett's,"
Lilliburlero, old Uncle Sam.
"Lero, lero, that leaves me zero,
That leaves me zero," says Uncle Sam,
"Lero, lero, filibuster-o,
That leaves me zero," says Uncle Sam.

6. "And by the way, one little thing more,"
Lilliburlero, old Uncle Sam,
"You're to refund the costs of the war,"
Lilliburlero, old Uncle Sam.
"Lero, lero, just what I fear-o,
Just what I fear," says old Uncle Sam,
"Lero, lero, filibuster-o,
Just what I fear," says old Uncle Sam.

7. "Next, you must own our Cavalier blood!"
Lilliburlero, old Uncle Sam,
"And that your Puritans sprang from the mud!"
Lilliburlero, old Uncle Sam.
"Lero, lero, that mud is clear-o,
That mud is clear," says old Uncle Sam,
"Lero, lero, filibuster-o,
That mud is clear," says old Uncle Sam.

8. "Slavery's, of course, the chief corner-stone,"
Lilliburlero, old Uncle Sam,
"Of our new civ-il-i-za-tion!"
Lilliburlero, old Uncle Sam.
"Lero, lero, that's quite sincere-o,
That's quite sincere," says old Uncle Sam,
"Lero, lero, filibuster-o,
That's quite sincere," says old Uncle Sam.

9. "You'll understand, my recreant tool,"
Lilliburlero, old Uncle Sam,
"You're to submit, and we are to rule,"
Lilliburlero, old Uncle Sam.
"Lero, lero, aren't you a hero!
Aren't you a hero," says Uncle Sam,
"Lero, lero, filibuster-o,
Aren't you a hero," says Uncle Sam.

10. "If to these terms you fully consent,"
Lilliburlero, old Uncle Sam,
"I'll be Perpetual King-President,"
Lilliburlero, old Uncle Sam.
"Lero, lero, take your sombrero,
Off to your swamps," says old Uncle Sam,
"Lero, lero, filibuster-o,
Cut, double quick!" says old Uncle Sam.

A "Horse Marine" of the C. S. A.

Spirit of the South.

Clear the Track

Words: Jesse Hutchinson
Music: "Old Dan Tucker,"
by Daniel D. Emmett

The Original Hutchinson Family Quartet (From an old lithograph)

It represented the railroad in characters of living light and song, with all its terrible enginery and speed and danger. And when they (the Hutchinson Family Singers) came to the chorus cry that gives name to the song—when they cried to the heedless pro-slavery multitude that were stupidly lingering on the track, and the engine "Liberator" coming hard upon them, under full steam and all speed, the Liberty Bell loud ringing and they standing like deaf men right in its whirlwind path, the way they cried "Get off the track!" in defiance of all time and rule was magnificent and sublime.

—*Nathaniel P. Rogers, in Abolitionist Newspaper, "Herald of Freedom" (circa 1846).*

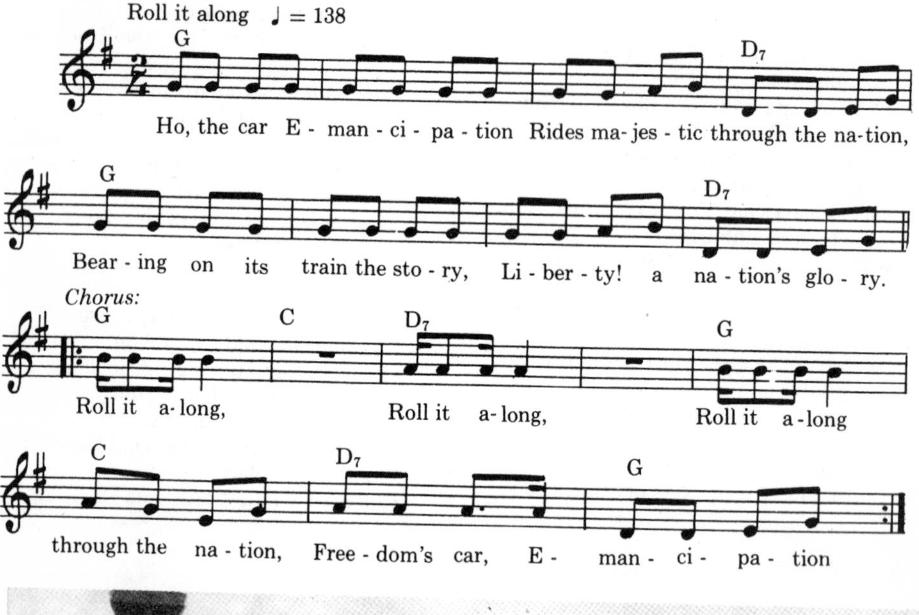

2. Men of various predilections,
Frightened, run in all directions;
Merchants, Editors, Physicians,
Lawyers, Priests and Politicians.
Get out of the way! Every station,
Clear the track for 'mancipation.

3. All true friends of Emancipation,
Haste to Freedom's Railroad Station;
Quick into the cars get seated,
All is ready and completed.
Put on the steam! All are crying,
And the Liberty Flags are flying.

4. Now again the Bell is tolling,
Soon you'll see the car wheels rolling;
Hinder not their destination,
Chartered for Emancipation.
Wood up the fire! Keep it flashing,
While the train goes onward dashing.

5. Hear the mighty car wheel's humming!
Now look out! *The Engine's coming!*
Church and Statesmen! Hear the thunder!
Clear the track! Or you'll fall under.
Get off the track! All are singing,
While the Liberty Bell is ringing.

6. On triumphant, see them bearing,
Through sectarian rubbish tearing;
The Bell and Whistle and the Steaming
Startles thousands from their dreaming.
Look out for the cars! While the Bell rings,
Ere the sound your funeral knell rings.

7. See the people run to meet us;
At the depots thousands greet us;
All take seats with exultation,
In the car Emancipation.
Huzza! Huzza! Emancipation
Soon will bless our happy nation

Lincoln's Funeral Train

Tenting on the Old Camp Ground

Words and music by Walter Kittredge

By the bivouac's fitful flame,
A procession winding around me, solemn and sweet and slow—but first I note,
The tents of the sleeping army, the fields' and woods' dim outline,
The darkness lit by spots of kindled fire, the silence,
Like a phantom far or near an occasional figure moving,
The shrubs and trees (as I lift my eyes they seem to be stealthily watching me).
While wind in procession thoughts, O tender and wondrous thoughts,
Of life and death, of home and the past and loved, and of those that are far away;
A solemn and slow procession there as I sit on the ground,
By the bivouac's fitful flame.

—*Walt Whitman*

2. We've been tenting tonight on the old camp ground,
Thinking of days gone by,
Of the loved ones at home that gave us the hand,
And the tear that said, "Goodbye!" (Chorus)

3. We are tired of war on the old camp ground,
Many are dead and gone,
Of the brave and true who've left their homes,
Others been wounded long. (Chorus)

4. We've been fighting today on the old camp ground,
Many are lying near;
Some are dead and some are dying,
Many are in tears.

Final Chorus:

Many are the hearts that are weary tonight,
Wishing for the war to cease;
Many are the hearts that are looking for the right
To see the dawn of peace.
Dying tonight, dying tonight,
Dying on the old camp ground.

The Bonnie Blue Flag

Words by Harry McCarthy
Music: "The Irish Jaunting Car"

Come, brothers! rally for the right!
The bravest of the brave
Sends forth her ringing battle-cry
Beside the Atlantic wave!
She leads the way in honor's path;
Come brothers, near and far,
Come rally round the Bonnie Blue Flag
That bears a single star.
—*Annie Chambers Ketchum*

2. As long as the Union was faithful to her trust,
Like friends and brethren, kind were we, and just;
But now, when Northern treachery attempts our rights to mar,
We hoist on high the Bonnie Blue Flag that bears a single star. (Chorus)

3. First gallant South Carolina nobly made the stand,
Then came Alabama and took her by the hand;
Next, quickly, Mississippi, Georgia, and Florida,
All raised on high the Bonnie Blue Flag that bears a single star. (Chorus)

4. Ye men of valor gather round the banner of the right,
Texas and fair Louisiana join us in the fight;
Davis, our loved President, and Stephens statesmen are;
Now rally round the Bonnie Blue Flag that bears a single star. (Chorus)

5. And here's to brave Virginia, the Old Dominion State.
With the young Confederacy at length has linked her fate.
Impelled by her example, now other States prepare
To hoist on high the Bonnie Blue Flag that bears a single star. (Chorus)

6. Then here's to our Confederacy, strong we are and brave,
Like patriots of old we'll fight, our heritage to save;
And rather than submit to shame, to die we would prefer,
So cheer for the Bonnie Blue Flag that bears a single star. (Chorus)

7. Then cheer, boys, cheer, raise a joyous shout,
For Arkansas and North Carolina now have both gone out;
And let another rousing cheer for Tennessee be given,
The single star of the Bonnie Blue Flag has grown to be eleven. (Chorus)

Goober Peas

Anonymous

The Colonel of an Alabama regiment was famous for having everything done up in military style. Once, while field officer of the day, and going his tour of inspection, he came on a sentinel from the eleventh Mississippi regiment sitting flat down on his post, with his gun taken entirely to pieces, when the following dialogue took place:

Colonel: "Don't you know that a sentinel while on duty, should always keep on his feet?"

Sentinel: (without looking up) "That's the way we used to do when the war first began; but that's played out long ago."

Colonel: (beginning to doubt the man is on duty) "Are you the sentinel here?"

Sentinel: "Well, I'm sort of a sentinel."

Colonel: (grimly) "Well, I'm a sort of officer of the day."

Sentinel: "Well, if you'll hold on till I sort of git my gun together, I'll give you a sort of a salute."

2. When a horseman passes, the soldiers have a rule,
To cry out at their loudest, "Mister, here's your mule!"
But another pleasure enchantinger than these,
Is wearing out your grinders, eating goober peas! (Chorus)

3. Just before the battle the Gen'ral hears a row,
He says, "The Yanks are coming, I hear their rifles now."
He turns around in wonder, and what do you think he sees?
The Georgia Militia—eating goober peas! (Chorus)

4. I think my song has lasted almost long enough,
The subject's interesting, but rhymes are mighty rough,
I wish this war was over, when free from rags and fleas,
We'd kiss our wives and sweethearts and gobble goober peas! (Chorus)

WAITING FOR HIS BREAKFAST. FROM A WAR-TIME SKETCH.

The Battle of Shiloh Hill

Words by M. B. Smith
(Company C, 2d Regiment, Texas Volunteers)
Music: "Wandering Sailor"

Skimming lightly, wheeling still,
The swallows fly low
Over the field in clouded days,
The forest-field of Shiloh—
Over the field where April rain
Solaced the parched ones stretched in pain
Through the pause of night
That followed the Sunday fight
Around the church of Shiloh—
The church so lone, the log-built one,
That echoed to many a parting groan
And natural prayer
Of dying foemen mingled there—
Foemen at morn, but friends at eve—
Fame or country least their care:
(What like a bullet can undeceive!)
But now they lie low,
While over them the swallows skim.
And all is hushed at Shiloh.

—Herman Melville (Apr. 1, 1862)

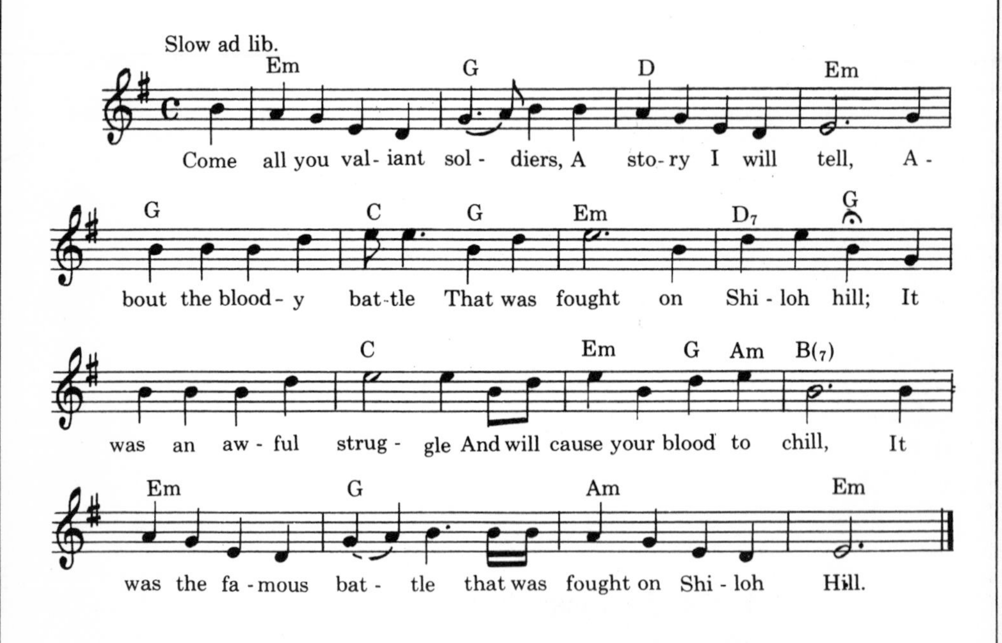

2. It was the Sixth of April,
   Just at the break of day,
   The drums and fifes were playing
   For us to march away;
   The feeling of that hour
   I do remember still,
   For the wounded and the dying
   That lay on Shiloh Hill.

3. About the hour of sunrise
   The battle it began,
   And before the day had vanished
   We fought them hand to hand;
   The horrors of the field
   Did my heart with anguish fill,
   For the wounded and the dying
   That lay on Shiloh Hill.

4. There were men from every nation
Laid on those bloody plains,
Fathers, sons, and brothers
Were numbered with the slain,
That has caused so many homes
With deep mourning to be filled,
All from the bloody battle
That was fought on Shiloh Hill.

5. The wounded men were crying
For help from everywhere,
While others, who were dying,
Were offering God their prayer,
"Protect my wife and children
If it is Thy holy will!"
Such were the prayers I heard
That night on Shiloh Hill.

6. And early the next morning
We were called to arms again,
Unmindful of the wounded
And unmindful* of the slain,
The struggle was renewed
And ten thousand men were killed;
This was the second conflict
Of the famous Shiloh Hill.

7. The battle it raged on,
Though dead and dying men
Lay thick all o'er the ground,
On the hill and on the glen;
And from their deadly wounds
The blood ran like a rill;
Such were the mournful sights
That I saw on Shiloh Hill.

8. Before the day was ended
The battle ceased to roar,
And thousands of brave soldiers
Had fell to rise no more;
They left their vacant ranks
For some other ones to fill,
And now their mouldering bodies
All lie on Shiloh Hill.

9. And now my song is ended
About those bloody plains,
I hope the sight by mortal man
May ne'er be seen again;
But I pray to God, the Saviour,
"If consistent with Thy will,
To save the souls of all who fell
On bloody Shiloh Hill."

SHILOAH MEETING HOUSE

Lorena

Words by Rev. H. D. L. Webster
Music by J. P. Webster

By the flow of the inland river,
Whence the fleets of the iron have fled,
Where the blades of the grave-grass quiver,
Asleep are the ranks of the dead;
Under the sod and the dew,
Waiting the judgement-day;
Under the one, the Blue,
Under the other, the Gray.
—*Francis Miles Finch*

2. A hundred months have passed, Lorena,
Since last I held that hand in mine,
And felt the pulse beat fast, Lorena,
Though mine beat faster far than thine.
A hundred months, 'twas flowery May,
When up the hilly slope we climbed,
To watch the dying of the day,
And hear the distant church bells chime.

3. We loved each other then, Lorena,
More than we ever dared to tell;
And what we might have been, Lorena,
Had but our lovings prospered well—
But then, 'tis past, the years are gone,
I'll not call up their shadowy forms;
I'll say to them, "Lost years, sleep on!
Sleep on! nor heed life's pelting storms."

4. The story of that past, Lorena,
Alas! I care not to repeat,
The hopes that could not last, Lorena,
They lived, but only lived to cheat.
I would not cause e'en one regret
To rankle in your bosom now;
For "if we *try,* we may forget,"
Were words of thine long years ago.

5. Yes, these were words of thine, Lorena,
They burn within my memory yet;
They touched some tender chords, Lorena,
Which thrill and tremble with regret.
'Twas not thy woman's heart that spoke;
Thy heart was always true to me:
A duty, stern and pressing, broke
The tie which linked my soul with thee.

6. It matters little now, Lorena,
The past is in the eternal past;
Our heads will soon lie low, Lorena,
Life's tide is ebbing out so fast.
There is a Future! O, thank God!
Of life this is so small a part!
'Tis dust to dust beneath the sod;
But there, *up there,* 'tis heart to heart.

The bivouac fire at the outposts of our army on the Potomac

Maryland, My Maryland

Words by James R. Randall
Music: "Tannenbaum"

I can scarcely control myself while I am writing you. I am boiling over with indignation. I once prayed for peace; but now, next to begging the blessing of God, I pray—"Hurrah for Jeff Davis and the Southern Confederacy!" and, woman as I am, if I knew the way, I would walk out of Maryland, until my foot rested upon more Southern soil. . . . Here there are hearts that beat as warm to the South as ever throbbed at the guns of Charleston. We are not conquered and *never will be;* and God grant that before long the flag of secession may wave over our city and State.

—*Letter from a Baltimore girl to a Charleston friend, May 16, 1861.*

2. Hark to an exiled son's appeal,
   Maryland, my Maryland!
   My Mother State, to thee I kneel,
   Maryland, my Maryland!
   For life or death, for woe or weal,
   Thy peerless chivalry reveal,
   And gird thy beauteous limbs with steel,
   Maryland, my Maryland!

3. Thou wilt not cower in the dust,
   Maryland, my Maryland!
   Thy beaming sword shall never rust,
   Maryland, my Maryland!
   Remember Carroll's sacred trust,
   Remember Howard's warlike thrust,
   And all thy slumberers with the just,
   Maryland, my Maryland!

4. Come! 'tis the red dawn of the day,
   Maryland, my Maryland!
Come! with thy panoplied array,
   Maryland, my Maryland!
With Ringgold's spirit for the fray,
With Watson's blood at Monterey,
With fearless Lowe and dashing May,
   Maryland, my Maryland!

5. Dear mother, burst the tyrant's chain,
   Maryland, my Maryland!
Virginia should not call in vain,
   Maryland, my Maryland!
She meets her sisters on the plain,
"Sic temper!" 'tis the proud refrain
That baffles minions back amain,
   Maryland, my Maryland!
Arise in majesty again,
   Maryland, my Maryland!*

6. Come! for thy shield is bright and strong,
   Maryland, my Maryland!
Come! for thy dalliance does thee wrong,
   Maryland, my Maryland!
Come to thine own heroic throng
Stalking with liberty along,
And chant thy dauntless slogan-song,
   Maryland, my Maryland!

7. I see the blush upon thy cheek,
   Maryland, my Maryland!
But thou wast ever bravely meek,
   Maryland, my Maryland!
But lo! there surges forth a shriek,
From hill to hill, from creek to creek,
Potomac calls to Chesapeake,
   Maryland, my Maryland!

8. Thou wilt not yield the vandal toll,
   Maryland, my Maryland!
Thou wilt not crook to his control,
   Maryland, my Maryland!
Better the fire upon thee roll,
Better the shot, the blade, the bowl,
Than crucifixion of the soul,
   Maryland, my Maryland!

9. I hear the distant thunder-hum,
   Maryland, my Maryland!
The "Old Line's" bugle, fife, and drum,
   Maryland, my Maryland!
She is not dead, nor deaf, nor dumb;
Huzza! she spurns the northern scum—
She breathes! She burns! She'll come!
   She'll come!
Maryland, my Maryland!

* The last two lines of verse 5 do not fit the music, but they appear in the original Randall poem.

The Rebel army crossing the fords of the Potomac for the invasion of Maryland

Cumberland Gap

Southern mountain folksong

Very few of the commissioned officers were religious. The large proportion of the soldiers were wicked and many were reckless. For more than a year very few manifested any desire to become Christians save the sick or wounded.

—*Confederate Chaplain who wintered with the Rebel troops in Cumberland Gap, 1861-1862, from his Diary.*

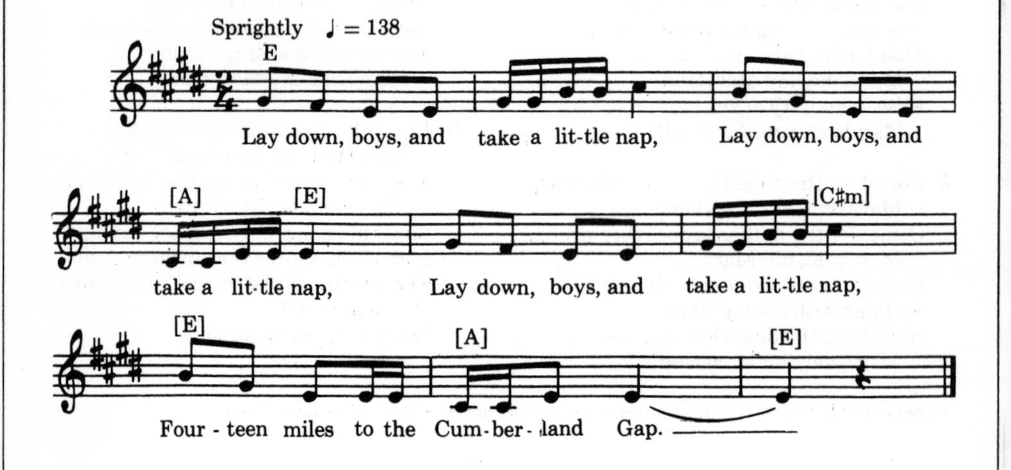

1. The first white man in Cumberland Gap,
   The first white man in Cumberland Gap,
   The first white man in Cumberland Gap,
   Was Doctor Walker, an English chap.

2. Daniel Boone on Pinnacle Rock,
   He killed Indians with an old flintlock.

3. Cumberland Gap is a noted place,
   Three kinds of water to wash your face.

4. Cumberland Gap with its cliff and rocks,
   Home of the panther, bear, and fox.

5. September mornin' in sixty-two,
   Morgan's Yankees all withdrew.

6. They spiked Long Tom on the mountain top,
   And over the cliffs they let him drop

7. They burned the hay, the meal, and the meat,
   And left the Rebels nothing to eat.

8. Braxton Bragg with his Rebel band,
   He run George Morgan to the blue-grass land.

9. The Rebels now will give a little yell,
They'll scare the Yankees all to Hell.

10. Ol' Aunt Dinah, ef you don't keer,
Leave my little jug settin' right here.

11. Ef it's not here when I come back,
I'll raise Hell in Cumberland Gap.

12. Ol' Aunt Dinah took a little spell,
Broke my little jug all to Hell.

13. I've got a woman in Cumberland Gap,
She's got a boy that calls me "pap."

14. Me and my wife and my wife's grand'pap,
All raise Hell in Cumberland Gap.

General Burnside's army occupying Cumberland Gap

Give Us a Flag

Words: anonymous
Music: "Hoist Up the Flag"
(by Billy Holmes)

Wouldn't no general but one take the colored boys. General Peg-Leg Butler, he say, "I'll take 'em." An' you know why? 'Cause his cavalry didn't have nothin' but black horses, an' them white men didn't look right on black horses. Put them Negroes on black horses, an' they just look right. Look like I can see them boys now. After they fight the fust battle, then ev'y general in Lincoln's army wanted 'em. They was the braves' soldiers the Yanks ever had.

—*A Negro veteran of the Civil War, interviewed by workers of the Federal Writers Program (WPA) in Virginia in the 1930's.*

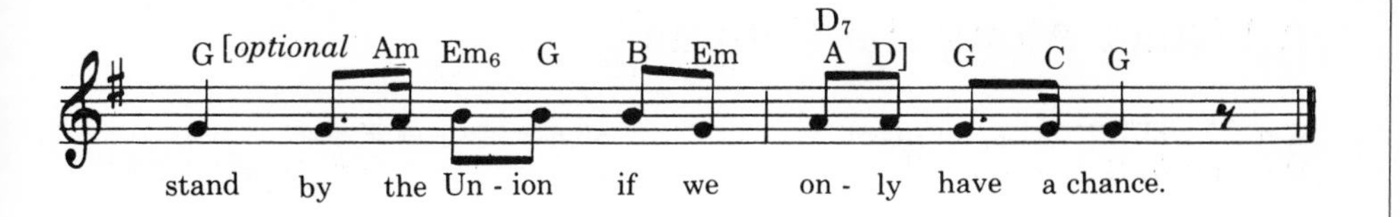

2. McClellan went to Richmond with two hundred thousand brave;
   He said, "Keep back the niggers" and the Union he would save.
   Little Mac he had his way, still the Union is in tears,
   NOW they call for the help of the colored volunteers. (Chorus)

3. Old Jeff says he'll hang us if we dare to meet him armed,
   A very big thing, but we are not at all alarmed;
   For he first has got to catch us before the way is clear,
   And that is "what's the matter" with the colored volunteer. (Chorus)

4. So rally, boys, rally, let us never mind the past;
   We had a hard road to travel, but our day is coming fast;
   For God is for the right, and we have no need to fear,
   The Union must be saved by the colored volunteer. (Chorus)

5. Then here is to the 54th, which has been nobly tried,
   They were willing, they were ready, with their bayonets by their side,
   Colonel Shaw led them on and he had no cause to fear,
   About the courage of the colored volunteer. (Chorus)

All Quiet Along the Potomac

Words by Mrs. Ethel Lynn Beers
Music by W. H. Goodwin

"All quiet along the Potomac. A picket shot."
—*War Dept, announcement, September, 1861.*

Brave sentry on your lonely beat,
May these blue stockings warm your feet;
And when from wars and camp you part,
May some fair knitter warm your heart.
—*Civil War comfort note*

2. All quiet along the Potomac tonight,
Where the soldiers lie peacefully dreaming,
Their tents in the rays of the clear autumn moon,
O'er the light of the watch fires, are gleaming;
A tremulous sign, as the gentle night wind,
Through the forest leaves softly is creeping,
While stars up above, with their glittering eyes,
Keep guard for the army is sleeping.

3. There's only the sound of the lone sentry's tread,
As he tramps from the rock to the fountain,
And thinks of the two in the low trundle bed,
Far away in the cot on the mountain.
His musket falls slack, and his face, dark and grim,
Grows gentle with memories tender,
As he mutters a prayer for the children asleep,
For their mother, may Heaven defend her.

4. The moon seems to shine just as brightly as then,
That night when the love yet unspoken
Leaped up to his lips when low-murmured vows
Were pledged to be ever unbroken.
Then drawing his sleeve roughly over his eyes,
He dashes off tears that are welling,
And gathers his gun closer up to its place
As if to keep down the heart-swelling.

5. He passes the fountain, the blasted pine tree,
The footstep is lagging and weary;
Yet onward he goes, through the broad belt of light,
Toward the shades of the forest so dreary.
Hark! Was it the night wind that rustled the leaves?
Was it moonlight so wondrously flashing?
It looks like a rifle—"Ah! Mary, good-bye!"
And the lifeblood is ebbing and splashing.

6. All quiet along the Potomac tonight,
No sound save the rush of the river;
While soft falls the dew on the face of the dead—
[*Skip to last beat of fourth from last measure*]
The picket's off duty forever.

Grafted into the Army

Words and music by Henry C. Work

> It's a rich man's war and a poor man's fight.
> —*Slogan of the Draft Rioters, New York City, 1863.*

2. Dressed up in his unicorn, dear little chap,
They have grafted him into the army;
It seems but a day since he sot in my lap,
But they grafted him into the army.
And these are the trousies he used to wear,
Them very same buttons, the patch and the tear;
But Uncle Sam gave him a bran' new pair
When they grafted him into the army.
(Chorus)

3. Now in my provisions I see him revealed,
They have grafted him into the army;
A picket beside the contented field,
They have grafted him into the army.
He looks kinder sickish—begins to cry,
A big volunteer standing right in his eye!
Oh, what if the ducky should up and die,
Now they've grafted him into the army.
(Chorus)

Process of drafting in the 6th District in New York, August 19

Roll, Alabama, Roll

Traditional (adapted by Hermes Nye)

THE CONFEDERATE CRUISER "ALABAMA."

The Alabama had the usual quota of wits and fun-makers among her crew. An Irish fiddler on board is the life of the forecastle. When the men are off-duty he sets them dancing to his lighter strains, or, dividing them into Northerners and Southerners, like a true Irishman, he gets up a sham fight to the spirit-stirring strains of a march, in which the Northerners are, of course, invariably beaten. Another sailor, Frank Townshend, is no mean poet, as will be be seen from the verses which here follow. He had sung the exploits of their beloved ship to his messmates in rude and vigorous fashion.

—*from the diary of an Officer on The Alabama.*

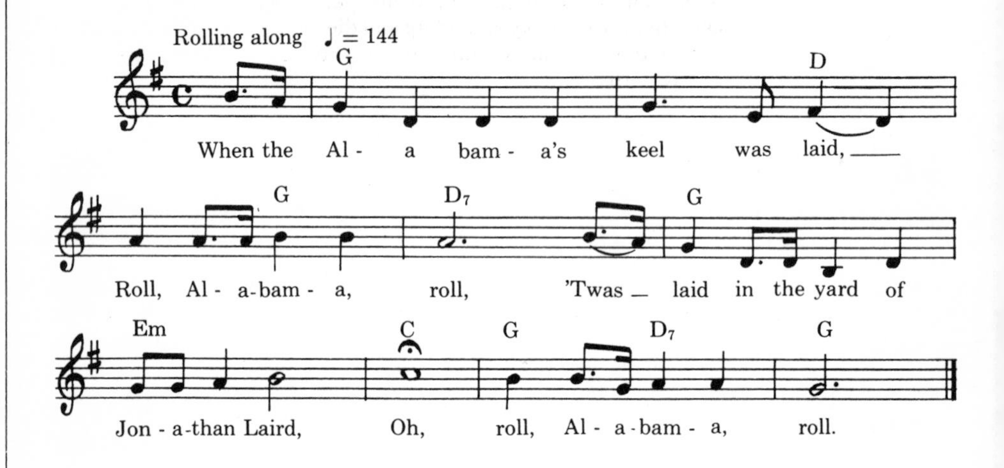

2. 'Twas laid in the yard of Jonathan Laird,
   Roll, Alabama, roll.
   'Twas laid in the town of Birkenhead,
   Roll, Alabama, roll.

3. Down the Mersey ways she rolled then,
   Roll, Alabama, roll.
   Liverpool fitted her with guns and men,
   Roll, Alabama, roll.

4. From the Western Isles she sailed forth,
   Roll, Alabama, roll,
   To destroy the commerce of the North,
   Roll, Alabama, roll.

5. To Cherbourg port she sailed one day,
   Roll, Alabama, roll,
   To take her count of prize money,
   Roll, Alabama, roll.

6. Many a sailor lad he saw his doom,
   Roll, Alabama, roll,
   When the Ke-arsarge it hove in view,
   Roll, Alabama, roll.

7. Till a ball from the forward pivot that day,
   Roll, Alabama, roll,
   Shot the Alabama's stern away,
   Roll, Alabama, roll.

8. Off the three-mile limit in sixty-five,
   Roll, Alabama, roll,
   The Alabama went to her grave,
   Roll, Alabama, roll.

Many Thousand Gone

Traditional Negro spiritual

I'll tell you, it's this way. My master call me up, and order me a short peck of corn and a hundred lash. My friends see it, and is sorry for me. When they come to the praise-meeting that night they sing about it. Some's very good singers and know how; and they work it in—work it in, you know, till they get it right; and that's the way.

—*An explanation of how the slave songs were created, by an unidentified Negro slave, as reported by J. Miller McKim (1862) from a first-hand interview.*

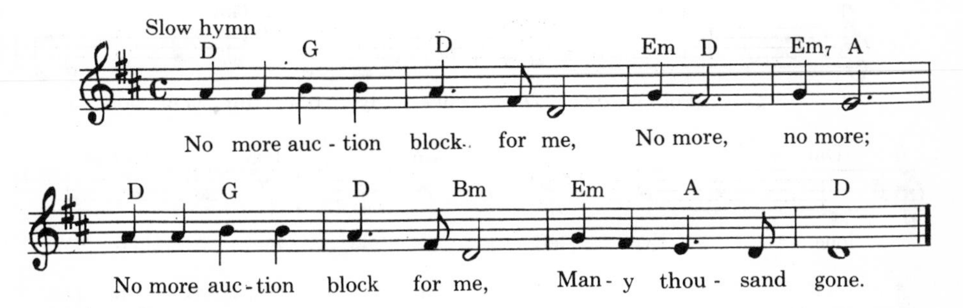

2. No more peck of corn for me,
   No more, no more;
   No more peck of corn for me,
   Many thousand gone.

3. No more driver's lash for me.

4. No more pint o' salt for me.

5. No more hundred lash for me.

6. No more mistress' call for me.

The Rebel Soldier

Southern Appalachian folk song
From the singing of Mrs. Lawson Grey

I will be for Jeffdavise till the tenisee river freezes over, and then be for him, and scratch on the ice:

> Jeffdavise rides a white horse,
> Lincoln rides a mule,
> Jeffdavise is a gentleman,
> And Lincoln is a fule.
>
> —*Letter from a Southern girl to her cousin, a prisoner-of-war at Camp Morton, Indianapolis.*

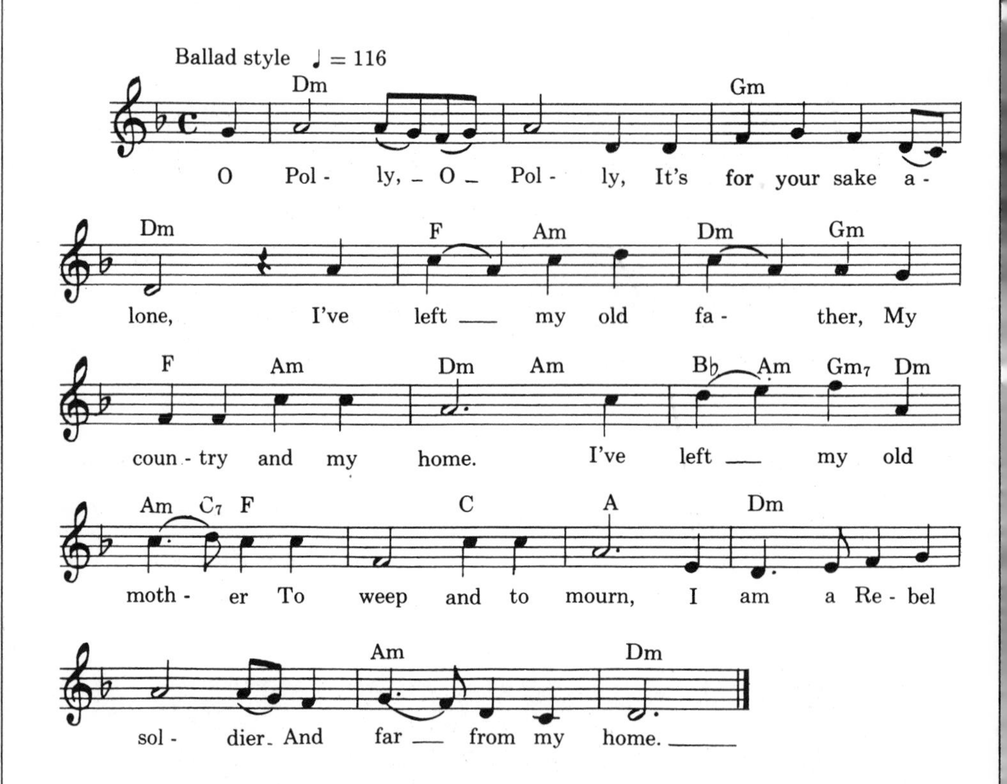

2. It's grape shot and musket,
   And the cannons lumber loud,
   There's many a mangled body,
   The blanket for their shroud;
   There's many a mangled body
   Left on the fields alone,
   I am a Rebel soldier
   And far from my home.

3. I'll eat when I'm hungry,
   I'll drink when I am dry,
   If the Yankees don't kill me,
   I'll live until I die;
   If the Yankees don't kill me
   And cause me to mourn,
   I am a Rebel soldier
   And far from my home.

4. Here's a good old cup of brandy
   And a glass of nice wine,
   You can drink to your true love,
   And I will drink to mine;
   And you can drink to your true love,
   And I'll lament and mourn,
   I am a Rebel soldier
   And far from my home.

5. I'll build me a castle on the mountain,
   On some green mountain high,
   Where I can see Polly
   As she is passing by;
   Where I can see Polly
   And help her to mourn,
   I am a Rebel soldier
   And far from my home.

The Gold Band

Traditional Negro spiritual

What gives the wheat fields blades of steel?
What points the Rebel cannon?
What sets the roaring rabble's heel
On the old star-spangled pennon?
What breaks the oath
Of the men of the South?
What whets the knife
For the Union's life?—
Hark to the answer: SLAVERY!

—John Greenleaf Whittier

2. Sister Mary goin' to hand down the robe,
In the army, bye and bye;
Goin' to hand down the robe and the gold band,
In the army, bye and bye. (Chorus)

Lincoln and Liberty

Words by Jesse Hutchinson
Music: "Rosin the Beau"

During a conversation on the approaching election in 1864, a gentleman remarked to President Lincoln that nothing could defeat him but Grant's capture of Richmond, to be followed by his (Grant's) nomination at Chicago and acceptance. "Well," said the President, "I feel very much like the man who said he didn't want to die particularly, but if he had got to die, that was precisely the disease he would like to die of."

—*The Civil War In Song and Story, Frank Moore, (1865).*

2. They'll find what by felling and mauling,
Our railmaker statesman can do;
For the people are everywhere calling
For Lincoln and Liberty too.
Then up with the banner so glorious,
The star-spangled red, white, and blue,
We'll fight till our banner's victorious,
For Lincoln and Liberty, too.

3. Our David's good sling is unerring,
The Slavocrat's giant he slew,
Then shout for the freedom preferring,
For Lincoln and Liberty, too.
We'll go for the son of Kentucky,
The hero of Hoosierdom through,
The pride of the "Suckers" so lucky,
For Lincoln and Liberty, too.

Who Will Care for Mother Now?

Words and music by Charles C. Sawyer

My God first, my country next, and then my family.

During one of our late battles, among many other noble fellows that fell, was a young man who had been the only support of an aged and sick mother for years. Hearing the surgeon tell those who were near him that he *could not live,* he placed his hand across his forehead, and with a trembling voice said, while burning tears ran down his fevered cheeks: *"Who will care for mother now?"*

—*From the preface to the printed sheet music (1863).*

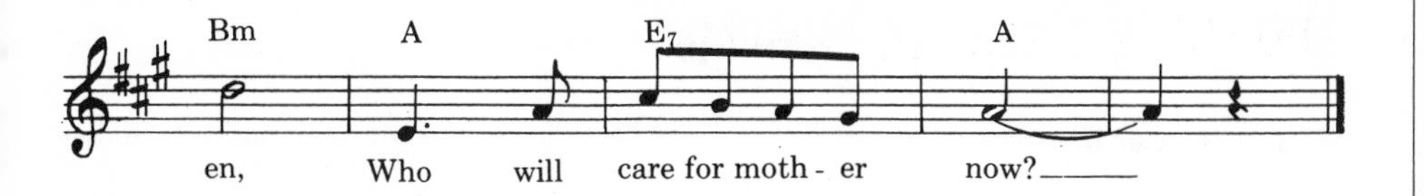

2. Who will comfort her in sorrow?
Who will dry the falling tear?
Gently smooth her wrinkled forehead?
Who will whisper words of cheer?
Even now I think I see her
Kneeling, praying for me! How
Can I leave her in anguish?
Who will care for mother now? (Chorus)

3. Let this knapsack be my pillow,
And my mantle be the sky;
Hasten, comrades, to the battle,
I will like a soldier die.
Soon with angels I'll be marching,
With bright laurels on my brow;
I have for my country fallen,
Who will care for mother now? (Chorus)

The Army of the Potomac. Burying the dead and burning dead horses at Fair Oaks Station, Virginia

Marching Through Georgia

Words and music by Henry C. Work

> I beg to present you as a Christmas gift, the city of Savannah, with one hundred and fifty guns and plenty of ammunition, also about 25,000 bales of cotton.
>
> —*William Tecumseh Sherman, a telegram to Abraham Lincoln, December 21, 1864.*

2. How the darkeys shouted when they heard the joyful sound!
How the turkeys gobbled which our commissary found!
How the sweet potatoes even started from the ground,
While we were marching through Georgia. (Chorus)

3. Yes, and there were Union men who wept with joyful tears,
When they saw the honored flag they had not seen for years;
Hardly could they be restrained from breaking forth in cheers,
While we were marching through Georgia. (Chorus)

4. "Sherman's dashing Yankee boys will never reach the coast!"
So the saucy Rebels said, and 'twas a handsome boast;
Had they not forgot, alas! to reckon with the host,
While we were marching through Georgia. (Chorus)

5. So we made a thoroughfare for Freedom and her train,
Sixty miles in latitude, three hundred to the main;
Treason fled before us, for resistance was in vain,
While we were marching through Georgia. (Chorus)

Virginia's Bloody Soil

Traditional
As sung by Frank Warner and
learned from "Yankee" John Galusha

There is many a boy here today who looks on war as all glory, but, boys, it is all hell. You can bear this warning voice to generations yet to come. I look upon war with horror.

—General William Tecumseh Sherman, address to G. A. R. Convention, Aug. 11, 1880.

2. When our good old flag, the Stars and Stripes, from Sumter's walls was hurled,
   And high o'erhead on the forwardest walls the Rebels their flag unfurled,
   It aroused each loyal Northern man and caused his blood to boil
   For to see that flag—Secession's rag—float o'er Virginia's soil.

3. Then from o'er the hills and mountain tops there came that wild alarm:
   Rise up! ye gallant sons of North, our country calls to arms!
   Come from the plains, o'er hill and dale, ye hardy sons of toil,
   For our flag is trampled in the dust on Virginia's bloody soil!

4. And thousands left their native homes, some never to return,
   And many's the wife and family dear were left behind to mourn.
   There was one who went among them who from danger would ne'er recoil;
   Now his bones lie bleaching on the fields of Virginia's bloody soil.

5. In the great fight of the Wilderness, where's many the brave men fell,
   Our captain led his comrades on through Rebel shot and shell;
   The wounded 'round they strewed the ground, the dead lay heaped in piles,
   The comrades weltered in their blood on Virginia's bloody soil.

6. The Rebels fought like fury, or tigers drove to bay;
They knew full well if the truth they'd tell they could not win the day.
It was hand to hand they fought 'em, the struggle was fierce and wild,
Till a bullet pierced our captain's brain on Virginia's bloody soil.

7. And now our hero's sleeping with thousands of the brave;
No marble slab does mark the place that shows where he was laid.
He died to save our Union, he's free from care and toil—
Thank God! the Stars and Stripes still wave above Virginia's soil!

Hold the Fort

Words and music by Philip Paul Bliss

Just before Sherman began his famous march to the sea in 1864, and while his army lay camped in the neighborhood of Atlanta on the 5th of October, the Army of Hood . . . passed the right flank of Sherman's Army, gained his rear, and commenced the destruction of the railroad leading north, burning blockhouses and capturing the small garrisons along the line. Sherman's Army was put in rapid motion pursuing Hood, to save the supplies and larger posts, the principal one of which was located at Altoona Pass. General Corse, of Illinois, was stationed here with about 1,500 men. . . . A million and a half of rations were stored here and it was highly important that the earthworks commanding the pass and protecting the supplies should be held. 6,000 men under command of General French were detailed by Hood to take the position. The works were completely surrounded and (the Union troops) summoned to surrender. Corse refused and a sharp fight commenced. The defenders were slowly driven into a small fort on the crest of the hill. Many had fallen and the result seemed to render a prolongation of the fight hopeless. At this moment an officer caught sight of a white signal flag far away across the valley, twenty miles distant, upon the top of Kenesaw Mountain. The signal was answered and soon the message was waved across from mountain to mountain:

"Hold the fort; I am coming.
—W. T. Sherman"

Cheers went up! Every man was moved to a full appreciation of the position, and under a murderous fire which killed or wounded more than half the men in the fort . . . they held the fort for three hours until the advance guard of Sherman's Army came up. French was obliged to retreat."

—*Major Whittle, speaking before a Sunday School meeting in Rockford, Illinois (1870), with Philip Paul Bliss in the audience.*

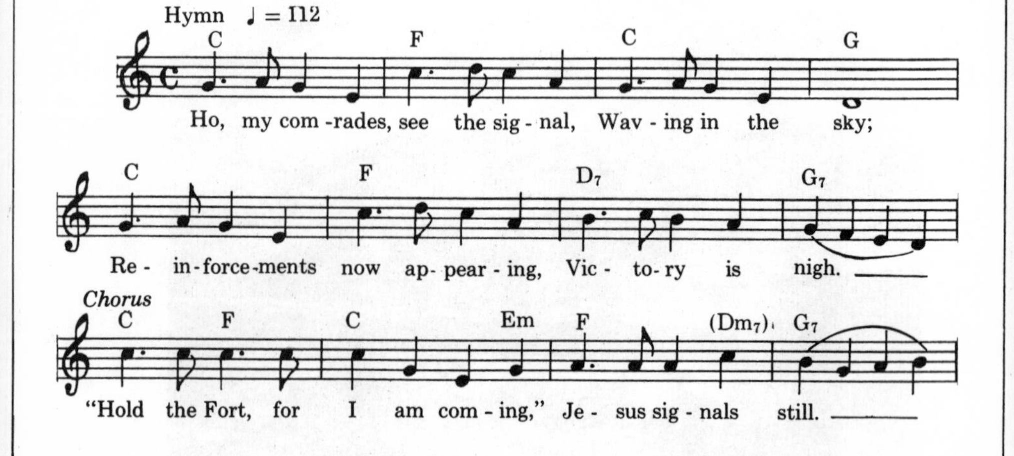

2. See the mighty host advancing,
   Satan leading on,
   Mighty men around us falling,
   Courage almost gone. (Chorus)

3. See the glorious banner waving,
   Hear the bugle blow,
   In our Leader's name we'll triumph
   Over every foe. (Chorus)

4. Fierce and long the battle rages,
   But our Help is near,
   Onward comes our great Commander,
   Cheer, my comrades, cheer. (Chorus)

Somebody's Darling

Words by Marie Ravenal de la Coste
Music by John Hill Hewitt

Dear Mother: I am here a prisoner of war, and mortally wounded. I can live but a few hours at farthest. I was shot fifty yards from the enemy's line. They have been exceedingly kind to me. I have no doubt as to the final result of this battle, and I hope I may live long enough to hear the shouts of victory before I die. I am very weak. Do not mourn my loss. I had hoped to have been spared; but a righteous God has ordered it otherwise, and I feel prepared to trust my case in His hands. Farewell to you all! I pray that God may receive my soul.

Your unfortunate son,
John

—*John Moseley (CSA), letter to his mother in Alabama, dated The Battlefield, Gettysburg, July 4, 1863.*

2. Matted and damp are his tresses of gold,
Kissing the snow of that fair young brow;
Pale are the lips of most delicate mould,
Somebody's darling is dying now.
Back from his beautiful purple-veined brow,
Brush off the wandering waves of gold;
Cross his white hands on his broad bosom now,
Somebody's darling is still and cold.
(Chorus)

3. Give him a kiss, but for Somebody's sake,
Murmur a prayer for him, soft and low;
One little curl from his golden mates take,
Somebody's pride they were once, you know;
Somebody's warm hand has oft rested there,
Was it a mother's so soft and white?
Or have the lips of a sister, so fair,
Ever been bathed in their waves of light?
(Chorus)

4. Somebody's watching and waiting for him,
Yearning to hold him again to her breast;
Yet, there he lies with his blue eyes so dim,
And purple, child-like lips half apart.
Tenderly bury the fair, unknown dead,
Pausing to drop on his grave a tear;
Carve on the wooden slab over his head,
"Somebody's darling is slumbering here."
(Chorus)

Tramp! Tramp! Tramp!

Words and music by George F. Root

The march of the 7th New York

The released prisoners of war are now coming up from the Southern prisons. I have seen a number of them; the sight is worse than any sight of battlefields or any collection of wounded, even the bloodiest. There was (as a sample) one large boat-load of several hundreds brought about the 25th to Annapolis; and out of the whole number, only three individuals were able to walk from the boat. The rest were carried ashore and laid down in one place or another.

—Walt Whitman

2. In the battle front we stood,
When their fiercest charge they made,
And they swept us off a hundred men or more,
But before we reached their lines,
They were beaten back dismayed,
And we heard the cry of vict'ry o'er and o'er.
(Chorus)

3. So within the prison cell
We are waiting for the day
That shall come to open wide the iron door,
And the hollow eye grows bright,
And the poor heart almost gay,
As we think of seeing home and friends once
more. (Chorus)

Oh, I'm a Good Old Rebel

Words ascribed to Major Innes Randolph, C.S.A.
Music: "Joe Bowers"

"Well, Johnny, I guess you fellow will go home now to stay," said one of Grant's men to one of Lee's veterans shortly after Appomattox.

But Johnny Reb wasn't having any. "Look here, Yank," he snapped. "You *guess*, do you, that we fellows are going home to stay? Maybe we are. But don't be giving us any of your impudence. If you do, we'll come back and lick you again."

—*From a story told by General John B. Gordon.*

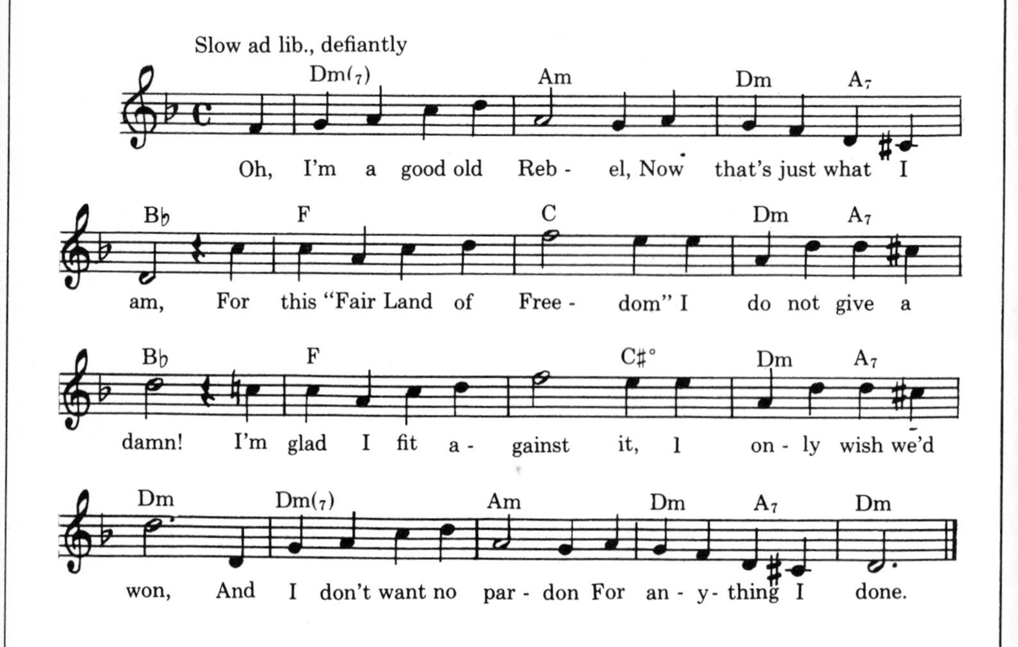

2. I hates the Constitution,
   This Great Republic, too,
   I hates the Freedman's Buro,
   In uniforms of blue;
   I hates the nasty eagle,
   With all his brag and fuss,
   The lyin', thievin' Yankees,
   I hates 'em wuss and wuss.

3. I hates the Yankee nation
   And everything they do,
   I hates the Declaration
   Of Independence, too;
   I hates the "glorious Union,"
   'Tis dripping with our blood,
   I hates their striped banner,
   I fit it all I could.

4. I followed old Marse Robert
   For four year, near about,
   Got wounded in three places
   And starved at P'int Lookout;
   I cotch the "roomatism,"
   A-campin' in the snow,
   But I killed a chance o' Yankees,
   I'd like to kill some mo'.

5. Three hundred thousand Yankees
   Is stiff in Southern dust;
   We got three hundred thousand
   Before they conquered us;
   They died of Southern fever
   And Southern steel and shot,
   I wish they was three million
   Instead of what we got.

6. I can't take up my musket
And fight 'em now no more,
But I ain't a-going to love 'em,
Now that is sarten sure;
And I don't want no pardon
For what I was and am,
I won't be reconstructed
And I don't care a damn!

Booth Killed Lincoln

Folk song
From the singing of Bascom Lamar Lunsford

The title of this ballad is "Booth," or "Booth Killed Lincoln." It's an old fiddle tune, and there are a few variants of the song. I heard my father hum it and sing a few of the stanzas when I was just a boy about six or ten years old.
—*Bascom Lamar Lunsford,*
folksinger of South Turkey Creek,
North Carolina

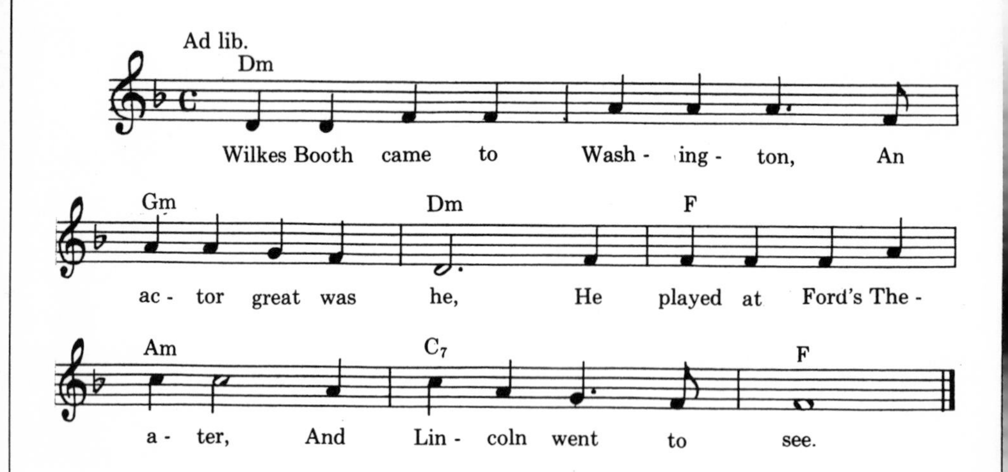

2. It was early in April,
   Not many weeks ago,
   The people of this fair city
   All gathered at the show.

3. The war it is all over,
   The people happy now,
   And Abraham Lincoln
   Arose to make his bow;

4. The people cheer him wildly,
   Arising to their feet,
   And Lincoln waving of his hand,
   He calmly takes his seat.

5. And while he sees the play go on,
   His thoughts are running deep,
   His darling wife, close by his side,
   Has fallen fast asleep.

6. From the box there hangs a flag,
   It is not the Stars and Bars,
   The flag that holds within its folds
   Bright gleaming Stripes and Stars.

7. J. Wilkes Booth he moves down the aisle,
   He had measured once before,
   He passes Lincoln's bodyguard
   A-nodding at the door.

8. He holds a dagger in his right hand,
   A pistol in his left,
   He shoots poor Lincoln in the temple,
   And sends his soul to rest.

9. The wife awakes from slumber,
   And screams in her rage,
   Booth jumps over the railing
   And lands him on the stage.

10. He'll rue the day, he'll rue the hour,
    As God him life shall give,
    When Booth stood in the center of the stage,
    Crying, "Tyrants shall not live!"

11. The people all excited then,
    Cried everyone, "A hand!"
    Cried all the people near,
    "For God's sake, save that man!"

12. Then Booth ran back with boot and spur
Across the backstage floor,
He mounts that trusty claybank mare,
All saddled at the door.

13. J. Wilkes Booth, in his last play,
All dressed in broadcloth deep,
He gallops down the alleyway,
I hear those horses feet.

14. Poor Lincoln then was heard to say,
And all has gone to rest,
"Of all the actors in this town,
I loved Wilkes Booth the best."

Kingdom Coming

Words and music by Henry C. Work

Secession Cavalry.

It is a false notion that slaves are contented if they are not beaten, and have enough to eat. Liberty is just as sweet to them as it is to us. I can say, from the bottom of my heart, may we never come to any terms with the rebels till this blot of slavery is wiped out. I, for one, would be willing to stay here ten years, and endure any amount of hardship, if at the end I could see America truly free. If the war could only accomplish this object, it seems as if I could say, "Now let Thy servant depart in peace."

—*Private William Fuller, 18th Regiment, Mass. Volunteers (1861).*

2. He's six foot one way, two foot the other,
And he weighs three hundred pounds,
His coat's so big, he couldn't pay the tailor,
And it won't go half way 'round.
He drills so much they call him 'Captain,'
And he got so dreadful tanned,
I expect he'll try and fool them Yankees
For to think he's contraband. (Chorus)

3. The people feel so lonesome living
In the loghouse on the lawn,
We moved our things to master's parlor
For to keep it while he's gone.
There's wine and cider in the kitchen,
And we will all have some;
I suppose they'll all be cornfiscated
When the Lincoln soldiers come. (Chorus)

4. The overseer he made us trouble,
And he drove us 'round a spell;
We locked him up in the smokehouse cellar,
With the key thrown in the well.
The whip is lost, the handcuff broken,
But master will have his pay;
He's old enough, big enough, ought to've
known better
Than to went and run away. (Chorus)

The Union army entering Richmond, April 3, 1865

When Johnny Comes Marching Home

Words and music by Patrick S. Gilmore

> I pass my days—and my nights, partly—at this window. I am sure our army is silently dispersing. Men are going the wrong way all the time. They slip by now with no songs or shouts. They have given the thing up.
>
> —*Diary entry, March 30, 1865, Chester, South Sarolina, Mary Boykin Chesnut.*

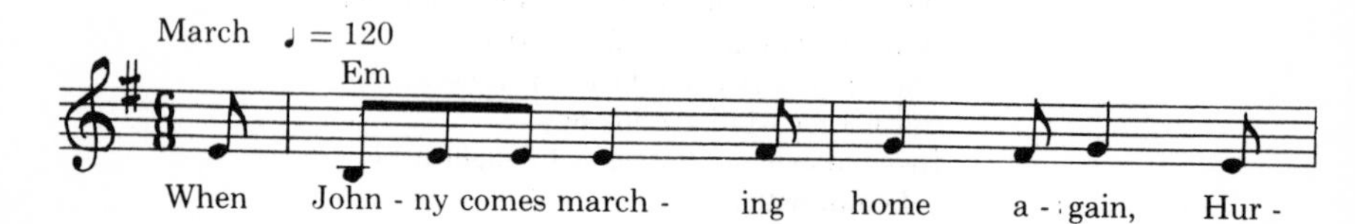

2. The old church bell will peal with joy,
   Hurrah, hurrah!
   To welcome home our darling boy,
   Hurrah, hurrah!
   The village lads and lassies say,
   With roses they will strew the way,
   And we'll all feel gay when
   Johnny comes marching home.

3. Get ready for the Jubilee,
   Hurrah, hurrah!
   We'll give the hero three times three,
   Hurrah, hurrah!
   The laurel wreath is ready now
   To place upon his loyal brow,
   And we'll all feel gay when
   Johnny comes marching home.

4. Let love and friendship on that day,
   Hurrah, hurrah!
   Their choicest treasures then display,
   Hurrah, hurrah!
   And let each one perform some part,
   To fill with joy the warrior's heart,
   And we'll all feel gay when Johnny comes
   marching home.

Lincoln's funeral procession on Pennsylvania Avenue